CU00656212

WELLNESS
IS YOUR
BUSINESS

WELLNESS
IS YOUR
BUSINESS

A Step-By-Step Testing Method to Answer
Everyday Health Questions

JENNELL COOK

WELLNESS IS YOUR BUSINESS © Copyright <<2023>> Jennell Cook

All rights reserved. No part of this publication may be reproduced, distributed, or transmitted in any form or by any means, including photocopying, recording, or other electronic or mechanical methods, without the prior written permission of the publisher, except in the case of brief quotations embodied in critical reviews and specific other non-commercial uses permitted by copyright law.

Although the author and publisher have made every effort to ensure that the information in this book was correct at press time, the author and publisher do not assume and hereby disclaim any liability to any party for any loss, damage, or disruption caused by errors or omissions, whether such errors or omissions result from negligence, accident, or any other cause.

Adherence to all applicable laws and regulations, including international, federal, state, and local governing professional licensing, business practices, advertising, and all other aspects of doing business in the US, Canada, or any other jurisdiction, is the sole responsibility of the reader and consumer.

Neither the author nor the publisher assumes any responsibility or liability whatsoever on behalf of the consumer or reader of this material. Any perceived slight of any individual or organization is purely unintentional.

The resources in this book are provided for educational and informational purposes only. They should not be used to replace the specialized training and professional judgment of a health care or mental health care professional. It is not intended to replace or in any way be a substitute for conventional medical care (or veterinarian care) or to encourage its abandonment.

Neither the author nor the publisher can be held responsible for using the information provided within this book. Always consult a trained professional before deciding on treatment of yourself or others.

Always consult with your medical doctor (or veterinarian) regarding any health issues before acting upon any opinion or recommendation that we have expressed within this book.

The statements provided in this book have not been evaluated by the Food and Drug Administration (FDA) or Health Canada. Nor any products, services, or other methods mentioned are not intended to diagnose, treat, cure or prevent disease.

Every effort has been made to represent this Simple Health Test method and its potential as accurately as possible. Examples and testimonials in this book are not to be interpreted as promises or guarantees. Your results may vary. We do not claim that you will receive any health benefits whatsoever. Where specific examples are quoted from individuals, there is no assurance you will do as well.

For more information, email info@jennellcook.com.

ISBN: 979-8-88759-382-1 - paperback
ISBN: 979-8-88759-383-8 - ebook

Claim Your Free Gift!

To help you achieve the best possible experience using the method in this book, I have found that wellness coaches, practitioners, and businesses have found this **Companion Guide** helps them stay focused on the steps that will find the answers quickly that move their clients and customers to results!

20 + Pages
Bonus Material
Additional Information
Track Your Results Forms
Space for Notes
And more!

You can receive your FREE copy today by visiting:
www.jennellcook.com/companion-guide

Access your exclusive bonus video for
a visual demonstration at:
www.jennellcook.com/bonus-video

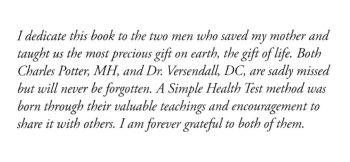

I dedicate this book to the two men who saved my mother and taught us the most precious gift on earth, the gift of life. Both Charles Potter, MH, and Dr. Versendall, DC, are sadly missed but will never be forgotten. A Simple Health Test method was born through their valuable teachings and encouragement to share it with others. I am forever grateful to both of them.

CONTENTS

Part 4: Additional Resources

INTRODUCTION

I nearly lost my mother due to poor health and a system that failed her. She suffered from tremendous body pain and fatigue. I did not understand it at the time; I was just a child. I still believed health was simple: we get sick, go to a doctor who gives us medicine to take, and then we get better.

Thinking back, my mother would frequently visit her doctor and specialists too. She followed all their instructions and suggestions. She never missed an appointment and took her many medications as prescribed. Instead of recovering, she became progressively worse. Health had become complicated.

Once I became old enough to understand her multiple health issues, I spent time worrying, afraid I could lose my mother. Disturbing thoughts plagued me of how she could miss our precious moments: my graduation, my wedding, and even the birth of my children someday. I knew we needed a solution, a doctor, or a magic pill to make my mother well again.

Then the turning point happened. I was 15 years old. My friend and I were walking down the streets of a small town outside our own. We saw a sign in one of the windows that said "psychic readings" and decided to go in. Neither of us knew much about it, but it sounded fun and something we wanted to try.

The woman giving the reading seemed very good. But then, I had no reference to compare. After a while, our conversation led to my mother. Her skills as a reader became impressive at this point. She told me about a man, an herbalist, Charles Potter, who lived in our hometown. She firmly believed Charles could help my mother. Maybe it was desperation. I didn't even know what an herbalist was, but I knew my mother needed to see him.

Next came the tricky part: convincing my mother to see a man we didn't know who does things we've never heard of, recommended by a psychic I had just met. Mom was not too convinced. So, I did what any teenage girl would do and called for Dad. Thankfully, my dad's support and common sense did the trick. "You're not well," he said. "What you are doing isn't working, and you're getting worse. What harm would it do to keep an open mind and try something new?" Dad asked.

That afternoon, Mom called Charles and arranged to meet with him. Much to my surprise, he said she could come right over! There is no future appointment for someday, and no referral is necessary from someone else. It was all very uncomplicated so far. I was highly optimistic and quickly ran to gather what Mom needed to get in the car without further delay or time to change her mind.

It was a short drive to see Charles. I tried to imagine him as we pulled in front of the high-rise building. Mom parked the car. We took a long walk until we found the elevator to ride up. I recall the smell in the hallway—an unusual combination of scents. I had not spent time in apartment buildings before.

The elevator doors opened, and we finally arrived. When Charles stepped out to greet us, I was surprised to see he was an older man. With his snow-like hair, and tall, slender build, he spoke in a very kind and soft manner.

After some paperwork, minor chit-chat, and a few questions, Charles got started. He explained that he used energy and demonstrated unique skills we had never seen before and knowledge we never knew. Charles "tested" my mom, using only his hands, no devices, machines, or equipment. I was utterly in awe.

Charles discussed the imbalances he discovered, in ways even I could understand, and how they showed up as weaknesses in my mom's body. All very accurate for her. He recommended supplements and vitamins not manufactured by drug companies and sold through practitioners. He offered easy solutions to improve her overall health and well-being; this made sense to us like nothing else.

Recommendations Charles gave included minor diet changes and foods to avoid based on his findings. He explained how her health could balance, and her body could naturally heal given the proper nutrition without drugs, surgeries, or side effects. It sounded so gentle when my mother's experiences had only been difficult.

My mom started on all of Charles' recommendations. She began to recover immediately, noticing subtle shifts and positive changes, while more complex issues took some time to resolve. The fatigue would end, and eventually, the pain would subside as her body returned to a more normal state. She began to feel like herself again and even participate in life, something she had almost forgotten how to do. Something I didn't remember her ever doing.

My mom's incredible health journey—particularly her recovery—ignited something inside her. I can still see the image as if it were only yesterday. She would sit in bed late at night with her favorite pajamas on, eating popcorn. I could see an intense look in her eyes, studying with pen in hand and books spread out all around her. She followed her calling to become a healer in the footsteps of the practitioner who saved her. But her journey would not stop there.

After a while, Mom and I began traveling together for more specialized learning. Soon to be blessed with knowledge and tools beyond what once seemed possible. Mom transitioned from trading her services for a loaf of homemade bread to opening a family health-food store and clinic. We added organic food items and pet therapies, brought in other practitioners and guest speakers, and taught wellness classes.

Today, my youngest daughter has assisted in making additional impressive discoveries using this method. Her inquisitive nature often challenged me, leading to remarkable new insights such as long-distance testing and healing and even finding solutions when products were unavailable. These abilities have become extremely important.

This family's journey and wellness success is now the inspiration for this book, an online course, in-person workshops, and a health mini-series of books and videos, all coming soon. Please stay in touch and share your success stories using this method. The world needs this and practitioners like you, now more than ever. My mother is 83 years old and continues to work doing what she loves. She is happy and healthy, living life her way, while so many today cannot do the same and need to be cared for by others.

PART 1

The Basics

MY STORY

I have not been without health issues myself. I came into this world suffering from breathing difficulties that interfered with my life. The shortness of breath would limit me from running and playing outside. But so much more than that. I would experience breathing attacks during the night, leaving me very afraid, waking up and feeling as though I was running out of air, wondering if I could even find my next breath.

My mother would fill the bathtub with hot water, allowing the steam to fill the room. As was once believed, this would help. Later I discovered that the cold night air helped me more. The many nights I would quietly take the stairs to find my sister, waking her in fear. She never made me feel bad and would get up despite how tired she likely was herself. She would take me somewhere outside and comfort me with her encouraging words as I listened to her soothing voice, breathing in the cool night air. Yes, this is what helped me.

Symptoms later changed from the nighttime horror of limited oxygen to the daytime trauma of shortness of breath. I would find myself attempting to catch my breath multiple times a day and far more susceptible to childhood conditions like croup. Pneumonia too.

I recall one of the worst attacks as if it were yesterday. I came running down the stairs from my room. My mom, sitting in the living room, immediately called Charles. I could tell from the shakiness in her voice that she was afraid too and then the relief when he answered her distress call, asking her to take me straight to him.

Charles brought me in and motioned for me to lie on the table. I was afraid because I couldn't breathe, and lying down was difficult; my instinct was to sit up. He placed his large hand over my neck and kept it there. Soon my breathing softened and became less forced. He taught me that the left hand is the healing hand, which allowed my breathing to return to normal. I felt such a sense of peace and comfort.

Charles explained that my chronic ritual of 'sighing' to catch my breath was an imbalance he found in my thyroid. I followed through with his simple recommendation and quickly felt the positive change.

Later in life, when I became a young mother myself, I took a more profound interest in health and learned to use food as medicine. Focusing on my thyroid, I discovered a simple recipe to continue its management through this diet.

Nutrition was expensive. As a single mom, I learned about gardening and how to grow our food. I love gardening, and the benefits were far more significant than I had ever expected they would be. I even taught wellness classes in our local community about food and shopping with health in mind for low-income single parents.

It was around this time when Charles introduced us to another practitioner, Dr. Versendall. We called him Dr. V., a brilliant chiropractor, energy worker, and healer we came to know and love. His extraordinary technique took our health to even higher levels than we knew were possible. He encouraged me to share his work and often mailed his notes to my home after his weekend seminars.

It was Dr. V who discovered a weakness in my lungs. A lung injury, he said. The specialized nutrition he recommended worked exceedingly well. Within that year, I never had another episode again. I began to exercise and even joined a gym. My dog and I would cycle 16-kilometer round trips on the weekends. It was transformational for me to be able to do such things when short sprints in school were so challenging. And my mother's incredible turnaround by that time left me stunned.

Here is a short list of my mother's health issues at that time so you can better understand her painful, worn-out existence.

She suffered from the following:

- Arthritis
- Bursitis
- A diseased mitral valve in her heart
- Thyroid dysfunction
- Breathing difficulties
- Anxiety
- Deteriorating kidneys (suspected from the number of medications)

These things also troubled her.

- She had part of her sacrum surgically removed
- She had part of her tailbone surgically removed
- She stretched her bladder three times (this is how they once handled recurring infections)
- Heavy narcotics were prescribed, often leaving her unable to function
- Finally, she was assigned a psychiatrist because they said she must be crazy due to always complaining and never being satisfied with her results

Doctors, drugs, and specialists were doing what they thought was best to help her with these many complex issues, and in the end, this method saved her. These Simple Health Tests enabled us to successfully navigate wellness for ourselves, our children, siblings, grandchildren, great-grandchildren, and even our pets. It allowed us to build a business that supported us financially, and more importantly, helped thousands of customers and clients on their health journeys.

Today I bring our Simple Health Test method to practitioners and store owners who focus on wellness. Our world is in troubling times. And despite the tremendous medical advances, the world is sicker than ever and needs you. This method will help you to pinpoint what your clients and customers need to transform their health beyond the management of it.

Teaching this method has been the most rewarding part of my life. Beautiful relationships were created by spending time with our customers in the store. I remember the excitement I felt, waiting to open up shop for the next customer to demonstrate our method, always knowing our Simple Health Test would guide them to purchase products that matched their expectations. Saving them money on items they didn't need often turned customers into clients, and many clients became our life-long friends.

Now that you know the intimate details that brought a Simple Health Test to life, let's discuss this method as it relates to your business and practice and exactly how you will use it. The action steps you will learn to obtain the best health results possible using the least amount of effort. We start with covering the five big questions of who, what, where, why, when, and a little about how.

Are you ready to dive in? Let's go!

THE FIVE W'S

What is it?

A Simple Health Test is an energy testing method based on various healing arts I learned over decades of study. These include touch for health, specialized kinesiology, brain gym, herbalism, hypnotherapy, designed clinical nutrition, contact reflex analysis, wild edibles, color therapy, leadership academy including NLP skills, and healing with sound. While I did not invent any of these, I did develop my system by connecting the dots. I discovered what combination worked best to obtain the most desired health outcomes— finding patterns of what worked most often in situations.

You can undoubtedly learn any or all of these, as I did. You may be proficient in some of these already. If not, this book will save you the decades it took me and give the highlights in the most simplified way. You can start implementing this method by Monday morning if you read this book over the weekend. I will focus on what I learned from the two men who impacted our health the most; my dear friends, colleagues, and mentors, Charles Potter, MH, and Dr. Versendall, DC.

I learned that our bodies are electrical energy, every organ and system. Like the wiring of a house, power flows from place to place, connected to one central source. When there is an interruption—like blowing a breaker, indicating a weakness, imbalance, or overload—the flow stops.

This energy would be comparable to the body, with the flow of energy traveling throughout all systems and organs, creating a powerful source of information for us to access. You will experience this using our testing and discover that when there is an interruption in the energy flow recognized as a 'break' indicating weakness, imbalance, or even overload.

Let us focus on what this method can do for you. Most people are found somewhere on this wheel today and are waiting for a practitioner like you or a wellness business like yours to save them. Where would we have seen my mother on this wheel?

If you said everywhere, you would be correct!

Who can use this?

Any practitioner can use this Simple Health Test method regardless of their specialty. It does not matter if you have just started or have decades of experience; you can use this. You do not need a background in health to use this method; it can easily be a stand-alone service.

Perhaps you sell products like crystals, oils, herbs, or supplements. This Simple Health Test method pinpoints which product is the best remedy while helping you avoid the ones that are not. You will discover the products that could cause side effects and in what area of the body.

Here is a short list of businesses that would benefit from utilizing this method; the possibilities are endless:

- Wellness center
- Chiropractic Clinic
- Pet store
- Veterinarian office
- Crystal shop
- Dentistry
- Naturopathic
- Reiki
- Fitness facility
- Herbalist
- Health food store

This Simple Health Test method will pinpoint what your customer or client needs to transform their health and help you to make those decisions quickly and accurately with the least amount of time and effort, regardless of the type of business or practice you have.

Where and **when** can you use this?

You can use this method anywhere and at any time you choose. There are no restrictions; there are no limitations. There are no special tools or equipment required. You can use this at your home office, retail store, or clinic, even over Zoom! Yes, that is correct.

- Anywhere
- Anytime
- No tools or equipment are necessary
- Over Zoom
- Over the phone
- When you are sitting at a red light (really, I honestly do this and will tell you about this in a later chapter)
- In an email or when your client is not with you

Yes, you can perform a Simple Health Test even when your client is not present or physically with you. I refer to this as remote testing, which we cover in the online course, but I need you to know it is possible! In fact, over the past couple of years, it has been the preferred way over in-person visits. Another option would be to use a stand-in that you will learn to do in a later chapter.

Because this is an 'energy' testing method, I have included a 'troubleshooting' chapter for possibilities and immediate solutions. Still, these do not affect where or when you can use this testing method.

Why would you want to use this?

You are moving clients and customers toward wellness results with the least effort. This method is invaluable in helping to gain clarity and answers needed to solve problems and discover issues you may not have known existed. The deeper insight you acquire will assist in helping your clients achieve their optimum results, creating raving and loyal fans as you move them from the previous image of unwell around this new image to wellness.

Sometimes as business owners, we become bored doing the same stuff over and over. If this is true for you, trust me, your clients will love the new ideas. Here is your opportunity to do something new or different. And you can implement it right away. Have a little fun with it. It can be hard to compete in today's world; this will give you room for growth and new concepts that put you ahead of the curve before everyone else!

Use this Simple Health Test method as an opportunity to touch existing clients and customers by letting them know about a new product or added service you offer that is now available to them. It will reignite visits from past clients and customers and even reach new ones with a special announcement highlighting how they will benefit.

Reasons why you need to be using this method in your business or practice:

- As a stand-alone product
- Add to an existing practice
- Stand out from the crowd
- An upsell service
- A reason to reach out to existing customers
- An added source of income
- A way to reach new clients

The bottom line is that you want to obtain the best possible results for your clients and customers while earning an income. A win-win for you and your clients.

Currently, our health care, food, and nutrition are all questionable. This Simple Health Test method will serve as your backup plan in turbulent times. I am confident you will also discover many additional ways to use a Simple Health Test, as I have. Many of those stories I will be sharing with you in this book. I hope you will share yours With our growing community at www.jennellcook. com/testimonials.

How can you best use this method in your practice?

The image below describes several ways you can use this method in your practice, depending on the type of practice or business you operate and where you hope to branch out.

Here I have compiled a more descriptive list to dive deeper into specific areas beyond the products or services you might already provide. By the end of this book, you will be able to use this Simple Health Test method to quickly and easily navigate these types of issues and so much more!

- Solutions to knee pain
- How to help with thinning hair
- Test what level their heart is currently at
- Do they have a virus or the flu?
- Are these strawberries helping or hurting?
- Is this toothpaste right for them?
- Which multivitamin should I use, if any?

In a later chapter, you will learn an extraordinary way to score numbers, track progress, and gauge results. Discover how to easily move toward wellness by using a simple number system to guide you to optimum results.

Here is a working example of how this might look. Shortly after Mom and I met Charles Potter, Dad had a bad knee. He was very active, so having a knee issue at that time was a massive problem. Dad consulted with Charles to find an alternative solution to surgery. Surgery was the only viable option, according to his doctor, as I recall, at that time.

Charles discovered after testing my dad, which only took a minute or two, that he had gout in his knee. Before considering surgery, he recommended a diet change he believed would remedy his gout. A list of acidic foods dad would need to avoid that caused his condition, in addition to consuming half a cup of fresh cherries daily to remove the build-up of acid that created the pain and inflammation. He was to do this until the pain and swelling disappeared. And it did. Dad was back to cycling again in no time.

BUSINESS BONUSES

Bonus #1

I'm an avid gardener and love to cook. What I enjoy most is finding ways to heal using food. The key is knowing which foods help and which foods hurt. We can have that information in minutes using a Simple Health Test!

Having that information greatly benefited a client with erectile dysfunction. After a few Simple Health Tests, we determined which foods would benefit his condition and which would contribute to the problem. After examining the beneficial ingredients, I created a cereal bar that helped. It was so successful that I wrote a book on the subject, which will soon be released. You may discover incredible finds with the help of this method.

Bonus #2

Here are a few ways you will learn how to use a Simple Health Test to answer pet owners' questions about their pets' well-being. A fantastic idea and one that I hold very close to my heart. The internet can be a tremendous resource for information; equally, it can be a source of information that could go wrong.

Let's face it; many pet owners choose other avenues over a veterinarian for many reasons. Cost is number one in my experience. So, let's help where and when we can to sort out all of the possibilities while minimizing the potential risks.

I would love to see this method available in every pet store. Either as a paid service or trained staff members on the floor using a Simple Health Test to assist their customers.

This method you are about to learn can help pet owners by providing answers to questions like these:

- Can Athena the dog use this product to help her ear infection?
- Is Cleo the cat OK with this food?
- What pet treat is best for Oreo the rabbit?
- Will this pet remedy for itchy paws be helpful or hurtful?
- Can Troy the guinea pig use this pet bedding safely?
- Should Skittles the parrot have this vitamin?
- Which mineral block is best for Misha the mouse?

Bonus #3

A Simple Health Test can determine which dental products to use and which ones to avoid. An additional and unique service we provided in our clinic. One you will be able to offer, if you choose, by the time you finish this book.

This idea came about after a horrible experience in our store. A local high school student regularly passed our location on her way home. This particular day, she entered our store and collapsed onto the floor; almost as soon as she walked in. We searched her backpack to find her ID and contacted her mother. We learned she had been ill for some time and intended to stop and ask us for help one day.

When she returned for an appointment, our testing determined it was her dental work. We suggested replacing her old amalgam fillings. Her mother arranged for that, and her daughter did recover.

THREE MAIN STEPS

Now that we have answered the five 'W' questions, let's look at the three simple steps of a Simple Health Test. I have called it simple intentionally. Learning and implementing this method can be done over a weekend. You will first learn the basic mechanics and these three steps you will repeatedly use: Location, Magic Number, and Moving the Needle.

The Simple Health Test method

My journey as a practitioner in the field of natural health could not have been accomplished as well without this unique ability. It shaped our reputation and helped us stand out from the competition. Our clinic thrived from demonstrating to our customers this valuable method at the front of our store. A fantastic additional source of income: higher product sales and multiple bookings for our clinic.

I can only assume you picked up this book because you are a practitioner already or thinking about entering the field of wellness in some way. You may even have a similar story, too, like ours. That is often the case. We were typically the last resort during my career as a practitioner in alternative and natural methods. Clients and customers would come in with complex issues, reporting having tried everything already. If this sounds familiar to you, rest assured that this method pairs well with any existing profession and is equally great as a stand-alone product.

Today the number of people seeking solutions beyond what they currently know is trending, rising, and worth pursuing. This book will be your valuable resource and guide to revisit and refresh your mind anytime. And there are multiple ways in which you will be able to use it personally or in a business.

A shorter book with plenty of stories to help illustrate, covering only the parts you need without all the fillers many books contain. We will include the actions you repeatedly perform to immerse yourself and become confident, starting with a few mechanics and then jumping into the following three steps.

Step #1 – Location

Knowing the *location* of an issue is the first step and helps quickly zero in on areas of weakness or imbalance with high accuracy. You can use reflexology points, acupuncture points, or images on the internet that show anatomy; you likely already have multiple charts and diagrams in your study area. You will need no additional tools, equipment, or products to continue. This first step is to help you detect weaknesses or imbalances in any *location*. Sometimes even before your client is aware of their existence.

To demonstrate what I mean, I'll use this example. I found a weakness on one side of my client's face at the location of a tooth I had suspected. I suggested a product typically good as a natural antibiotic in these situations. His response to this was disbelief; it happens.

He explained that he felt nothing and that there was no issue as far as he knew or could feel. However, months later, he called to let me know an abscess had been discovered in the *location*, right where the testing indicated an issue, even though he was unaware of it himself at the time.

He had this to say later:

> "Jennell detected an issue on the left side of my face … I was in disbelief… but a few months passed, I woke up one day with the beginning of an abscess… that later required antibiotics and a root canal."
>
> ~ Ronald C.

Step #2 – Magic Number

Having a *magic number* makes the process easy for us by using a standard scale of 0–10 that your client or customer can understand. After locating a weakness or imbalance, we give it a *magic number*. This number indicates where we currently are using our scale, so we know how far we need to go for the result we want to achieve.

We also use our *magic numbers* to score and track progress. This way, you keep your records straight, goals on task, and always have the information to look back on. I suggest using a check-in sheet your customer or client can sign. Often, they forget how bad they were in the beginning before they came to see you. (This document and many more are all available to you in the online course.)

I recall this client who had an issue with her infant son. A Simple Health Test uncovered a weakness in Step #1, the *location* of his stomach. Several solutions could help her son: supplements, oils, and even foods, such as prunes, pears, or pineapple juice. Using Step #2, our *magic number*, was critical in finding the best solution possible from the list of options. In this case, one of the oils for digestion moved the needle the most, which you will learn next in Step #3.

This mom texted me after a few days and said;

> "He has pooped three times today! He usually poops once every four days."
> ~ Ashley

Step #3 – Move the Needle

A client's verbal feedback is essential, but we can have more data available using a Simple Health Test. As a practitioner in my field, I never had access to any specialized tools or equipment, which could have been helpful but also time-consuming and expensive. This method gave me the information I needed with the least amount of time and money spent to get the best results possible. You would agree that no matter what we do, we are *moving the needle* toward our wellness goal or further from our destination.

To demonstrate, I was hosting an event for an MLM company in the field of Wellness and Nutrition. Many people were invited, including some of my clients. A leader in my upline did a muscle test on a guest, who was also my client, indicating that a tea this company was selling was good for him. And although this was true, to a degree, I knew this product would not *move the needle* at all. Of course, signing up customers was the goal, but I had to demonstrate to my upline and assure my client I was operating with his health first. Additional testing indicated another product was his better option, as it *moved the needle*. Many items could test well, but we are looking for the best option using a Simple Health Test.

Each of these steps takes mere seconds to perform. That was not a typo; they require only seconds. Some of what you will be learning might be hard to believe. But I assure you, keep an open heart and mind to the possibilities, and you will help your clients achieve goals using a series of Simple Health Tests. Happy customers and clients equal great advertising, like these people:

> "I am still in awe of how much better my feet feel. I am so grateful."
> ~ B.B.

And this,

> "Hi, Jennell; thank you for your help with my back; I could do the drive and fish for over eight hours. Had a good sleep last night and woke up feeling normal."
> ~ Jeff

Now that you understand the three main steps and why you will want to use them, it's time to roll up your sleeves and take action. In the next chapter, we will begin with our first hands-on test, "Are you testable?" It is from this place that you will always start.

Are you ready to get to the doing part and use this method? Let's go.

ARE YOU TESTABLE?

Before we dive into the three main steps you just learned about in the previous chapter, we will take our first action step and learn a basic energy testing technique. It is these action steps that will lead you to the results. You may already be familiar with 'muscle testing' and may even use this in your practice now. In that case, you will find the first step easy.

As we progress further, the testing will differ, but the mechanics will be the same. If muscle testing is new to you, that's good; using a Simple Health Test won't have you unlearn anything you may do now. Either way, it is all positive, and you will master this primary first step.

You will always begin every testing session with your client or customer, whom we will call the *subject*, and 'check in' by asking, "Are you testable?" What exactly does this mean, and why should you do this?

Performing this step will ensure two essential factors:

1. Your subject has the ability or the electrical capacity, I call it, to do the test. Passing this test means the subject is, in fact, testable. (If the testing determines the subject is not testable, the troubleshooting chapter will walk you through how to correct this quickly.)

2. Allows your subject, who may be new to this method of energy testing, an opportunity to experience what to expect, what this will feel like, and how they can best assist you in making the testing process go smoothly.

Use this vital first step to work out any kinks or bugs immediately. Once you have that out of the way, you can focus on the outcome and the results you want to achieve together.

If you're ready, here we go.

Directions:

Here are the directions you will follow to check in and see if your subject is testable. You do this by asking, 'Are you testable?' by saying the words in your mind or asking out loud. It does not matter as long as you focus your intention on finding out if your subject is testable.

Now that you clearly understand where your thoughts need to focus, let's begin the actions and get you and your subject into the correct testing position. There are six basic steps, and They are as follows:

Testing position:

1. Have your *subject* (this is your customer or client that you intend to test) stand slightly *to the side* and not directly in front of you. This will ensure you are not in their energy field or personal space.

It would be challenging to perform if you stand directly in front of one another. (You will understand this part when you try it out yourself.)

- Have your subject extend *their* left arm, raising it to their side, parallel to the ground. (Not raised toward the ceiling too high, not pointing towards the ground too low, but lifted straight out, away from their body.)
- Place the pad of *your* index finger, of *your* left hand, between your subject's eyes, at the bridge of their nose, making only gentle contact. (Slow and steady, working near their eyes.)

Refer to the illustration for a helpful visual.

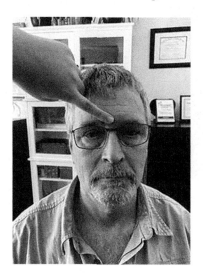

Side note: if you are left-handed, switch that up. It doesn't matter which hand you use, so long as you are comfortable. *Remember*, if you do so, you will also have to switch the rest, left vs. right, as we continue with the remaining instructions.

- Now, at the same time, you will place two or three fingers of your right hand slightly above your subjects' left wrist (the wrist of their extended arm) and *push* down (not too hard and not too soft) while instructing them to "resist your downward push." Please see the illustration below for a representation of what this looks like.

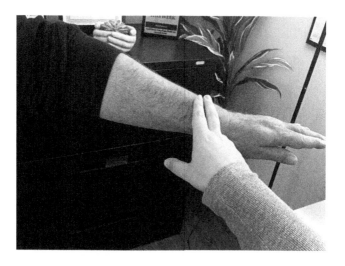

It is essential to explain that they should not be pushing back or lifting their arm; they are simply 'holding' their position.

At this point, your client will experience only one of two outcomes:

a) They *can* easily and comfortably resist your downward push.
b) They *cannot* easily and comfortably resist your downward push.

There is no in-between. This testing method is not a test of strength, so use only as much force as necessary, or their arm will quickly tire.

Let's now move on to number five.

Here, we will repeat what you have already learned in step three, but this time, instead of using the pad of your index finger, you will be using the *back of your index finger* or the nail side.

Reminder: you are still holding their wrist from step four and have yet to let go of the wrist. These moves take only a few seconds to complete from beginning to end.

It will look like this:

*   Place the nail side of your index finger of your left hand, gently making contact between your client's eyes at the bridge of their nose. Now you will *push* down once again, and at the same time, you will instruct your subject to "resist your downward push." Please refer to the illustration below for a visual.

- Simultaneously push down on their extended arm (using two or three fingers of your right hand, slightly above your subject's left wrist.)

Hot Tip #1

To do this fluently, turn your finger from the front (pad side) to the back (nail side). In other words, you are just flipping it from one side to the other without moving your arm, just your fingertip by turning your wrist.

You should immediately notice that one way will be easy for your subject to resist, and the other should be more difficult for them to resist. This part, steps 1–6, should take about three to five seconds to perform, so you have an idea of how fluid it is! It's honestly that quick and easy.

Hot Tip #2

If you need help differentiating between *weak* and *strong* using their arm or if they are not feeling a difference, you may need to exert more force initially, only once or twice, to demonstrate and feel the maximum distinction to help grasp the concept. The first few times will be a bit clunky, but subtleness will quickly develop as you both become comfortable knowing what to expect. I promise.

Many years ago, I did a seminar with a few hundred people who had never heard of this method before. I asked the most muscular man in the audience to come up and allow me to demonstrate that this was an energy test, not a test of muscle or strength. As you have already practiced using the basic 'are you testable' test, you discovered there are only two outcomes. One side of the index finger will be strong, and the other will be weak (either the pad side or the nail side), which means that this man from the audience I chose will be able to easily resist my downward push without any real effort at all. While the other side, when I roll my index finger over, he will not be able to easily resist my downward push without using force to do so.

We did the test. It looked like this. I got the man from the audience into our testing position, explained what I was looking for, then placed the pad of my index finger between his eyes and pushed while instructing him to resist. He easily resisted. I rolled my finger over and repeated the same steps. This time when I pushed down, his arm dropped, and he could not easily resist.

Without moving from our current position, I asked him to use his strength this time and resist my downward push harder, which he did. And still, he was not able to resist my downward push. Next, I asked him to fight even harder this time, using his full muscle strength! Of course, I also had to use more force when pushing down on his extended arm. This part of the testing is usually quite mind-blowing the first time someone experiences it.

We showed the audience that no matter how hard he tried, he would be unable to resist my downward push. He could barely resist, indicating this was not a test of strength. He was stronger than I was; that was obvious. Once you get the hang of things, and you will, this method requires no force and does not need to be difficult for you or your subject.

You have learned the basic testing mechanics and will continue to use this throughout. I encourage you to practice this to get the 'feel.' If you have had any issues up until now, don't worry; we have you covered in the next chapter with our troubleshooting guide. Read through this next chapter even if you found the basic testing mechanics easy to carry out. A day could come when you need a little troubleshooting help to test someone.

Access your exclusive bonus video for
a visual demonstration at:
www.jennellcook.com/bonus-video

TROUBLESHOOTING

Now that you have practiced and learned our basic testing technique, there are instances when you will encounter someone who is not currently testable. I often refer to this as 'nobody's home'; we need to find why and correct them using this troubleshooting guide.

When someone is not testable, the positive and negative tests at the bridge of the nose are the same. There is no change in the person's ability to resist the downward push comfortably.

<u>Side Note</u>: sometimes, even the practitioner is not testable. It's true. The person performing the test could also be affected by one or more of the following circumstances.

Below is a list of questions and their respective solutions that you can use to remedy this problem quickly. Go through this series of questions to determine the culprit (you can do this by having a conversation and directly asking them the following questions; it's that simple):

- Are you hydrated? (Or thirsty?)
- Are you hungry? (When did you last eat?)

- Are you a smoker and want a cigarette? (They have not had one at the time they usually would have.)
- Is the person wearing any device like a magnet?
- Are they low on energy, or do they have an energetic interference? We will explore this further in a moment.

Here are the suggested solutions to quickly remedy the above issues, in order:

- If hydration was an issue, drink water.
- Eat something; even a cracker could suffice for hunger.
- Smokers can put a cigarette in their mouth, but lighting it is unnecessary (smokers get their energy from cigarettes).
- Devices can be removed and then tested again.
- See below to increase (or change) one's energy, which could be interrupted for various reasons.

If energy is an issue, consider using the following options:

Option #1: Using both hands to the right and left of the client's collarbone, brush vigorously in a downward motion five to ten times or so.

Hot Tip: You can perform this on yourself. Cross your arms, put your fingers on each side of your collarbone and rub downwards briskly numerous times.

Option #2: I had a pair of magnetic insoles in my clinic that would work well. I would have my subject stand on them while I performed the necessary testing.

<u>Option #3</u>: A common cause is a sensitivity to EMFs (electromagnetic frequencies), which can interfere with energy testing. If I were out teaching a workshop somewhere, I would have the person hold my EMF device I always wear when teaching.

<u>Option #4</u>: As I recall, artificial lighting interfered with a student's ability to be tested, so we needed to move him to a different area in the room, away from the artificial light source.

Next, go back and re-test to see if you have a different result after trying each step; you will likely find the cause within one of these steps. (We cover additional causes and solutions in our online program, leaving no stone unturned, and also self-testing so you can keep yourself in perfect testing condition.)

You have learned about and even completed our initial Simple Health Test basics! This first action step is by far the most challenging. Getting the feel is the key. Once you have mastered this, you will, with practice. Let's celebrate and move on. First, take a moment to review a few of our essential takeaways, and when you are ready, we will move on to more intermediate steps where we see results happen.

Top 3 Takeaways

1. Fill in the blank. What should you always do first?

Make sure your subject is _____

_____

2. What is one thing you can try if your subject is not testable?

_____

_____

3. Name one way this method could benefit your business.

_____

_____

Your Challenge, If You Agree To Accept It:

Choose five people (clients, friends, or family members) and practice the 'are you testable' technique right now. Go! You've got this and then come back to our next level of learning intermediate skills. I accept _____ (Check here.)

PART 2

Intermediate Techniques

HOW TO TEST THINGS

Did you accept the challenge? If you did, you rock! Celebrate. Give yourself a big pat on the back. If you didn't take the challenge, do it now, and come back! Why? Because it helps you to learn. The power is in the action steps; take action now, celebrate, and come back.

We know how to determine if your client or customer is testable, so let's dive into the intermediate mechanics of testing things. We will look for the outcome that indicates whether something is helpful or hurtful. There is no neutral.

I recall teaching a class once where one of my students, proficient in muscle testing, believed that there were many neutral outcomes. After we practiced using the items on the table multiple times, his results indicated a positive (good) or negative (harmful) effect, with no neutral. Anything we can think of to test is either helping us or hurting us in some way. There is no neutral in my experience.

First, gather any items you believe would cause a strong or weak reaction and include products you might recommend. Even have items you believe should be eliminated from their diet. Whatever those things are, in any category, lay them all on a table (or the floor if they are large, and they might be).

Your collection of items could look like this:

- Potatoes
- Essential oils
- Toothpaste
- Cherries
- Cat fur
- Jewelry
- A mattress
- Crystals
- Herbs
- Banana
- Nutritional product
- Magnets
- Dental materials
- Ice Cream
- Tea
- Pet treats

Directions:

Reminder: we have already determined that the subject is testable and will continue testing from there. We will repeat this part often, so I will continue to remind you!

1. Choose an item from the table and have your subject hold it, put it in their pocket, or touch it with their foot or hand if it's too large.

Get into position:

2.   Have your subject stand slightly to the side, not directly in front of you.
     (Stay out of their personal space and energy field).

3.   Have your subject extend their left arm, raising it to their side, parallel to the ground.
     (Not raised toward the ceiling too high or pointing toward the ground too low. You are lifting straight out, away from your subject's body.)

4.   Place two or three fingers of your right hand slightly above the left wrist of your subject's extended arm. (Do not wrap your fingers around their wrist. You are not gripping their arm.)
     (Your left hand can be resting on the subject's shoulder.)

5.   Push down on their extended arm while instructing them to resist by asking them to "resist your downward push."

Once again, you are looking for strength or weakness, using the same technique you have already learned; to determine if they can easily resist your downward push. That's it.

Try these steps using a variety of items from the table to get a feel for the general idea of testing an object or a product. These will have you well on your way to making significant discoveries with your clients and customers. This critical intel about what is helping and what is hurting will help you guide them to results quickly and easily.

In a later chapter, we will dive into using numbers we call *frequency* using a sliding scale of zero through ten. You will learn which number is safe and when you should stay away from an item because of its number.

One day, my daughter came to the house for a visit. She had a terrible sore throat. She wanted to know if I had something she could take with her to use at home, and of course, I did. I suggested she look in my cabinet for the bottle I recommended. I should have taken a moment to test the bottle she took, but I didn't. Sometimes, I know the answers based on my knowledge or experience, but still, I'm only guessing. Until I perform a Simple Health Test, I don't know with any certainty.

As practitioners, we can sometimes work as if on autopilot. If I had followed through with the appropriate steps you are learning from this book, I would have known that this particular bottle was not good for my daughter. More on this story later, but for now, know that she got much worse.

THINK OUTSIDE THE BOX

Now that you have mastered the basic steps in our testing and successfully learned how to test various items, it's time to expand your mind and think outside the box. I can demonstrate best using the following example.

Let's say you're testing a client with apples. Are the apples cooked or raw? Are they red or green? Apple juice or apple sauce, sweetened or not? Thinking outside the box often helped me fine-tune our results, giving me additional information to make further changes. Sometimes, this thinking helps locate root causes and other underlying issues we may have overlooked.

A story about cauliflower comes to mind. A woman contacted me in distress after her husband ate his typical dinner. He primarily enjoyed his meat and potatoes with gravy. This time with fresh cauliflower as the side dish. Shortly after eating, he became uncomfortable. His discomfort quickly turned to pain. His abdomen swelled significantly. She asked me, after the fact, if I could test the various items on his plate for future reference. Of course, she assumed that the least healthy item would be the culprit. Much to our surprise, it was the fresh cauliflower. After further testing various types of cauliflower, we quickly discovered that only frozen cauliflower did not have the same negative outcome, nor did it ever produce the same bad result for him.

Here is a partial list of some of the questions we may need to ask; I'm sure you can add to it and come up with ideas of your own too. And remember this: "When in doubt, test it out!" What is suitable for one does not mean it is good for everyone, so remember to think outside the box. Here are a few examples:

- Cooked or raw
- Boxed versus canned
- Organic or not
- Fresh versus frozen
- Steamed, fried, or boiled
- Pet food: kibble, canned, or raw
- Test foods alone, not in combination
- Test foods at different times of the day, morning versus bedtime

When testing pet hair, test different types: Long versus short / Indoor versus outdoor cat hair

I always brought along the same items when teaching my workshops. For example, natural peppermint and mint toothpaste. Most people test with one or the other, usually not both. Same with regular carrots and the raw bagged mini carrots. These items are great for testing and demonstrating differences. We should be testing our food and the products we use.

Look For Additives

Test each ingredient when there are combinations, testing each one that might be a culprit. Keep records for future reference, keep an ongoing list of positive or negative outcomes, and include additives such as dyes, perfumes, waxes, or colors. Food is often the culprit or contributing to overall health and well-being. Take the time to test and know with certainty what is helping or hurting; remember the cauliflower guy!

There are also times when companies change their ingredients. I have had this happen with dog food. One subtle change could make all the difference. Check back with your clients. It provides another reason to see them again or offer an additional service and keep your records up to date. You will want to reconnect with them and continue helping them achieve the best possible results.

I recall the woman who was a big fan of tea tree oil. She used the oil often for many things. On this day, her husband reached out, pleading for my help, as something was wrong with his wife. He was panicking. I came right over as I lived nearby. I saw the woman; her face twisted like nothing I had ever seen. She could drink only using a straw. She had already been to her doctor and even her dentist with no luck. We determined through a series of questions that she was using a different brand of tea tree oil. Her specific brand was unavailable, and she purchased a different one. We tested the new tea tree oil and found this to be the culprit. Thankfully, her face fully returned to normal once we found and removed the cause.

What if you need to check an item and don't have it available for testing?

- Write it down and be specific
- Find an image in a magazine
- Print an image off the Internet

Consider these items too:

- Laundry soap
- Perfumes
- Makeup brushes
- Body wash
- Sunscreen

Anything can cause a good or bad response. Your job is to think outside the box sometimes and find what those things are. Use every opportunity to squeeze out any possibility to create a shift for your client or customer, moving them closer to their goals.

After a while, you will get very good at testing. Just like anything, it will become second nature. My oldest daughter required many chiropractic adjustments due to an injury. The problem was that she was afraid to have adjustments done to her. I remember learning an incredible technique from one of my mentors. He showed me how to correct subluxations safely by adjusting energetically; this is a hands-off approach. I used this technique on her often with great success. But after she moved away to college, I had no choice but to think outside the box.

I learned how to 'remotely' adjust her. I know it sounds crazy, but it worked. It worked so well that I began doing this for other clients too. I used it on myself multiple times after a boating accident years ago. I share this teaching in my online course and highly recommend knowing how to do this. Remote adjustments became a highly requested service. Here is what one client had to say:

> "I started having severe structural issues lately. It's always at the most inconvenient times, meaning a

chiropractor wasn't always available, or I could not get to one. Jennell was able to help. Through long-distance testing, she could not only determine my structural weaknesses but adjust them accordingly."

~ Joanne

You now understand the value of thinking outside the box. You may have already thought of clients or customers you can assist using this. In the next chapter, your mind reaches further to solve another kind of problem. What can you do if you cannot use your subject's arm for testing?

USING A STAND-IN FOR TESTING

While your mind is still thinking outside the box, consider this potential problem. There will be times when testing a client or customer that you run into a situation where you are not able to use your subject's arm; what can you do? There are several options. We will cover the most straightforward way here.

The fastest approach when you cannot use your subject's arm is to use a stand-in, as I call it. Using someone else's arm as a substitute to test your *subject* is a simple and effective solution when you cannot use the subject's arm for testing. Have them stand behind your subject and *use their arm* instead; this is one way. There are many others we teach in our course too.

Hot Tip #1

To save you even more time, use the arm of one of your trained staff members! (*I love live trainings. Reach out if you're interested in a private or group training session at info@jennellcook.com*)

Here is a list to demonstrate instances when you may need a stand-in:

- Your client has a shoulder injury
- You are asked to test a child or pet
- Virtual customers or clients using live cameras
- I often test clients over email without ever having met them by requesting a recent photograph (I teach this *remote testing* as a valuable part of the online course)

OK, let's get to the action steps for testing using a stand-in:

Directions:

Start by getting into the position you have done multiple times with your subject, except this time we will add your chosen stand-in. I know you already determined this person is testable, yes? Bravo!

1. Have your subject stand in front of you, slightly off to the side, to ensure you are not in their energy field.
2. Have your *stand-in* position themselves *behind your subject* and have them make contact with your subject.

Contact is made by having your stand-in place their right hand on the subject's shoulder. Physical contact in any form is all that is needed here.

The *stand-in* would be positioned slightly off the subject's left side so you can comfortably reach the arm of the stand-in you will be using for testing. (This would be *your* right, the mirror image.)

3. Have the *stand-in* extend their left arm, raising it to their side for you to use while remaining in contact with the subject. (Your subject can stand, sit, or even lie down.)

Refer to the illustration below for a helpful visual.

Hot Tip #2

Here are a few additional ways to make contact:

• When testing a small pet, I would have my client or customer hold the small animal. They would be my stand-in for that pet, and I would use their arm for testing.

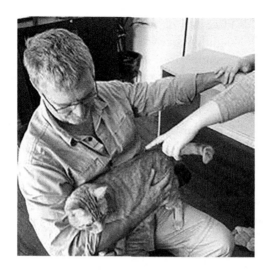

- With a larger animal, have your stand-in touch the animal anywhere; they can use their foot if necessary. This way, they don't have to bend down or bend over, making things awkward. The larger animal is presumably sitting or standing on the floor. Then you may continue and use their arm for testing.

- Let's say the pet owner is holding a small bunny for testing, and you cannot use the owner's arm for the test. This can be easily remedied. Have a stand-in behind the pet owner, with their hand on the owner's shoulder, and continue using the stand-in arm for testing, as outlined in step #3 above. Simple?

The following steps are nothing more than a rinse-and-repeat with the steps you have already learned. The difference is that you are using the arm of your stand-in to do them. To recap:

4. Place two or three fingers of your right hand slightly above your stand-in's left wrist (of their extended arm) and push down (not too hard, and not too soft) while instructing them to "resist your downward push."

Reminder: it is essential that the stand-in understands not to push back and lift their arm; they are simply 'holding' their position.

At this point, they will experience only one of two outcomes:

a) They *can* easily and comfortably resist your downward push.
b) They *cannot* easily and comfortably resist your downward push.

There is no in-between. This testing method is not a test of strength, so use only as much force as necessary, or their arm will quickly tire, and this is just the beginning of our testing sequence.

5. Place the nail side of your index finger of your left hand between your subject's eyes (you are testing your *subject*, not the stand-in) at the bridge of their nose, making only gentle contact.

Instruct your stand-in to "resist your downward push" as you simultaneously push down on their extended arm again.

Can the stand-in easily and comfortably resist your downward push? That's it. Wonderful. You have successfully learned how to use a stand-in when you cannot use a subject's arm. Now let's have a little more fun with the items on the table and learn how important it is to find an item's frequency in the next chapter.

FREQUENCY

Before we dive into frequency, I'd like to continue with the story about my daughter. Do you remember? Here's a refresher. While visiting one day, she mentioned having a sore throat and took a product from my office. I suggested she find one to bring home and use. But she got worse—much worse.

The rest of the story went like this: I should have followed the Simple Health Test steps but didn't. I knew my daughter was testable and aware of the issue we were dealing with, but I ended there and needed to follow through with the next important step: testing the items on the table! I allowed her to take the remedy without having tested it first.

I should have checked the item's frequency. I love this method because if you use the steps, there are so many backup plans built into it that you have multiple opportunities to find possible errors. You will learn how to do this in a moment.

As you learned in the previous chapter, testing the product is one important part. But we can now expand on that by determining an item's frequency, potency, or ability to use it effectively. For example, cherries are good for your health. They are an excellent remedy for inflammation in the body and pain. We know this. But how effective would they be if those cherries you intend to use have expired, gone rancid, were old, or otherwise harmful?

Ah ha! Like the remedy for my daughter's sore throat. If I had checked its frequency, I would have known it had lost its potency or was ineffective. It doesn't matter why. Either way, she recovered quickly and easily once we replaced this undesirable bottle. I gave her the identical product, only a bottle with an acceptable frequency.

Here are the steps to determine the frequency of an item.

Reminder: We have already determined that the subject is testable. We will continue from here. (If they are not, please refer to the troubleshooting chapter and then return here.)

1. Get into position; your subject stands slightly off to the side and not directly in front of you. (Stay out of their personal space and energy field).

2. Have your subject extend their left arm, raising it to their side, parallel to the ground. (Not raised toward the ceiling too high or pointing toward the ground too low. Lifted straight out, away from the body of your subject.)

3. Point to one of the items on your table.

4. Without direct contact with the item, *make your move*.

<u>Side Note</u>: To **make your move**, you will use your left hand and make a swift motion as if to swipe the item aside, or you can brush down on it (or any similar movement that would be the same type of gesture without making physical contact with the item,) in other words, it would look like you were waving your hand in the air *in front* of your chosen item without actually touching it.

(Remember, your 'intention' is to focus on checking this item for its *frequency* or number.)

5. Next, *pulse* using your subject's arm while simultaneously counting using a simple 0–10 scale.

<u>Side Note</u>: A **pulse** is performed with gentle arm pumping. It would look like this; one (push), two (push), three (push), and so on until the arm drops on a number.

You will recognize their arm drops because it will be as if the shoulder releases and allows the arm to fall. When that happens, the number at which their arm dropped will be the item's *frequency*. Write that number down.

If the *frequency* of an item is a 6 or below, I would stay away from this item and consider it not to be good. A frequency of 7–10 is within the acceptable range. Update your records of what your client or customer does not test well with and what you determined helpful. I recommend testing the products you bring into your store or clinic. Here's why.

While performing inventory tasks at our health-food store, I found a random item and wondered about it. I mentioned it to my mother, who explained that a customer returned it, stating that the item did not work for her. Of course, Mom and I were both a bit concerned and perplexed at the same time. Never had this happened. To ensure it was not a testing error, Mom used me as a stand in to test the woman who insisted on returning the product. Her testing was accurate regarding the issue and the chosen remedy. The missing step was testing the frequency of the product. It was never our habit to test new products just delivered; they were new!

To our amazement, this bottle was testing poorly for whatever reason. Therefore, it would not be suitable for anyone. As with my daughter's previous story, it just wouldn't do its intended job. We called the company, who was happy to replace the bottle. Lesson learned.

Now we have concluded our chapter on determining whether a product is good to use by checking its frequency. Well done! In the next chapter, there are bonus examples of digesting what you have learned in an actual working setting.

USING WHAT YOU HAVE LEARNED

You've come so far, let's pause to drive home what we've learned using some bonus examples before diving into our three main steps. I want you to envision how this can help you, your business, and your people.

Here is an example. You are a clinic specializing in weight-loss programs and products to support your clients (or even weight gain, also a problem for many people.) You educate your members about nutrition, diet, and products linked to their condition or goals. You offer classes about stress and how that relates to hormones that affect weight issues. You ask questions that target specifics and recommend programs you offer. Plus, you sell a wide range of products that help expedite client results. Everything from pills, bars, and shakes to meal replacements and even complete meals.

You will want to test in various ways. Test the products on the table. Will they help or hinder? Is this positive or negative, good or bad? When there is a known issue (weight loss, weight gain, digestion, appetite suppressant, etc.), focus your intent as you test the remedies on the table. A narrower focus can help you to be more accurate with your test results. We will explore deeper testing in a later chapter; let's review from here.

This process should only take a minute or two and will depend on the number of items or products you intend to test on the table. Here's what it looks like:

1. First, know that your subject is testable.
2. Next, get into position (your subject stands slightly to the side).
3. Choose the first product you would recommend.
4. Have your client make contact with the product.
5. Test the item(s).

Reminder: place the two fingers of your right hand two inches or so above the left wrist of their extended arm (do not wrap your fingers around their wrist. You are not gripping their arm).

6. Now push down while instructing them to "resist your downward push."

Again, you are looking for strength or weakness; can they easily resist your downward push? That's it. Repeat these steps using various products you wish to sell or recommend until you find the ones that work well and quickly eliminate the ones that do not.

In a later chapter, you will discover how to choose the *best* product to help get your client to their intended home run. We have been practicing using a variety of tests to give you more resources to draw from later.

Bonus Example #1

For example, you own a metaphysical store specializing in crystals. Your customer needs something to help them sleep. You test your customer with a particular stone while thinking about the specific circumstance they are inquiring about, such as their desire to improve their sleep. Again, it is your intention or what you think about while you are testing. Or in other words, make sure you are focused on their ability to improve their sleep while testing out the stone you recommend as a viable remedy!

Hot Tip: Whom are you testing? The person inquiring? Or is this a gift for someone else suffering from a sleep issue? (Hint: then you need a stand-in.)

One day my daughter came asking me to test her because she had been feeling very off. She wondered if her crystals and stones could be the cause. Using crystals was a recent interest and hobby she learned from social media to help promote study and learning. (Besides the obvious benefits of looking cute in her room, a decor thing many people enjoy!)

We did a Simple Health Test of all her crystals and stones and found one that did not test well at all. Ironically, she found it on our driveway, claiming it looked pretty! After removing the stone, she quickly returned to normal.

Bonus Example #2

Say you are in the pet-health-and-wellness industry. You sell various products to choose from for your customers, and you want to stand out from other stores while making an impact. You offer a testing service that helps customers quickly sort through conflicting data and make product selection more personal and beneficial to their pet's health, safety, and wellness. As a result of your unique service, they return to your store again and again.

Let me introduce you to Nigel. A young lady purchased this exotic fish from a local pet store. She was excited about choosing the fish and even bought herself the necessary supplies. You can imagine how she felt when only a short time later, Nigel seemed unwell. She looked hopeless when she asked for my help. Having yet to learn about fish anatomy, we began by testing the fish food and made a minor adjustment. Nigel became energetic and interested in food again; he was a happy fish with a delighted owner!

Hot Tip: Your customer or client will appreciate not having to spend money on multiple items that may or may not work until they find the one that *will*.

You completed our intermediate skills. Congratulations! Let's review a few of our essential takeaways and, if ready, move on to our final, more advanced aspects, and dive into our three main steps in a Simple Health Test.

Top Three Takeaways

1. Thinking outside the box, what are two ways to test apples?

    1. _____
    2. _____

2. Describe a situation that might require you to use someone else for testing. *(Hint: I call this a stand-in, why would you need to do this?)*

    _____

3. A frequency of 3 is a good number and is within the acceptable range, or in other words, positive for someone to use or consume.

    True or false? (Please circle your answer.)

    Your Challenge, If You Agree to Accept It:

Choose any item and find its *frequency*; please write it down.

Item: _____

Frequency: _____

I accept _____ (Please check here.)

Bonus Challenge, If You Agree To Accept It:

Use a stand in to find the *frequency* of one additional item; you can do this!

Item: _____

Frequency: _____

I accept _____ (Please check here.)

PART 3

Advanced
Practices

LOCATION

We are finally here! The three main steps are where the rubber meets the road. We make a real difference here for our customers and clients beyond what you have already done. If you have been performing the action steps, you have mastered the mechanics and various beneficial ways of using a Simple Health Test.

We start with determining where the issue is. The *location*, the cause, or the areas of concern? Find the imbalance or weakness—the root. Symptoms give you a clue about where to begin, and our testing method can help zero in on a more precise location. It can provide incredible insight and clarity as symptoms can often have many possibilities.

Here are some examples of locations that you can use to help your customers or clients:

- Thyroid condition
- Heart check-in
- Sudden knee pain
- Hair health
- Liver issue

You get the idea here. You can test any area or location on the body quickly. You likely already know dozens off the top of your head and can locate anatomy charts online if you don't have something similar already in your profession. The illustration below is an example of testing a location.

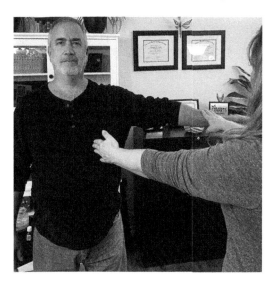

Let's say your client or customer comes to your clinic or store and is concerned about a kidney issue. Using the exact steps that you already know, let's go ahead and test the energy of their kidney health. We will add in a few little extras.

Here is a recap of how to begin:

1. Are they testable? We will presume they are in this case.
2. Get into the *testing position* with your subject.

We will use the left kidney to continue with our example for testing.

Hot Tip: If you need to know a *location*, you can look it up somewhere online, download a chart or resource and keep this handy for later reference.

<u>Remember</u>, if caught in the moment, your *intention is vital;* so long as you are in the general area and intend to test the left kidney in **this example**, you won't go wrong.

3. Point to the location of their left kidney using your left index finger (the area of their left kidney would be on your right because you are facing them, a mirror image—don't forget this part.)

Bonus Tip: The location of their left kidney is a little above the navel or belly button and slightly to the subject's left (your right).

4. Test to determine if their left kidney is strong or weak.

<u>Remember</u>: strong means they can comfortably resist your downward push, and weak indicates they cannot easily resist your downward push.

a) If the location is weak, then your assumption is correct; there is a weakness or imbalance in the left kidney that you need to address.

b) If the location is strong, you are done for now.

My younger daughter and I adopted a cat, a five-year-old orange tabby named Jack. A fantastic guy. Despite being dewormed at the shelter, he still arrived with a bad case of parasites (worms). It was an easy fix for me;

however, Jack had already begun passing his contagious parasites around to the rest of us in the home. I won't get too graphic, but my younger daughter was freaking out at the sight of it! As a result, we all got tested and treated accordingly. The location was the same for all of us, but the solutions differed. I love having certainty and 'knowing.'

Our online course will cover additional locations that come up often, but their location on the body is not as obvious to find, such as testing for the presence of kidney stones, blood clots, parasites, and yeast (candida).

Great job learning our first primary step, how to do a Simple Health Test for a particular location. In the next chapter, we will continue investigating why we want to test the left kidney further using our magic numbers.

FINDING YOUR MAGIC NUMBER

The first essential step you learned is determining the *location* of a weakness or imbalance. Our second step, equally vital, is finding the *magic number* to know where we currently are using a standard sliding scale of 0–10. To determine this, we will continue using our example of the left kidney.

Here is a **recap** of where we left off.

1. Are they testable? (Yes.)
2. Get into the 'testing position' with your subject.
3. Point to the location of their left kidney using your left index finger (remember the mirror image).

<u>Side note:</u> It does not matter if we tested the left kidney as weak or strong at this point; you will continue and find its magic number; there are two reasons why we want to do this:

a) You suspected a weakness there (the kidney in this case) and
b) It's good to learn this valuable skill for future reference.

Example: Suppose you want to 'check in' with a client or customer and know their heart health level for instance. By using our magic number test, you can check in anywhere at anytime!

4. *Make your move* (this means wave, brush down, or swipe to the side) over the location of the left kidney. (Remember to wave in the air, do not make contact with your subject.)
5. *Pulse* while simultaneously counting and asking with intention (out loud or to yourself) what the number of the left kidney is, using a simple 0–10 scale you already know.

It will look like this:

One (push), two (push), three (push), and so on until the arm drops on a number, and it will.

Remember, you will recognize when the arm drops because it will feel as if the shoulder releases and allows the arm to fall or rest, no longer able to stay raised or resist your downward motion comfortably. When that happens, you have found the *magic number*, the number their arm dropped on, and you will write that number down.

Let's say their magic number is 7. Is this an acceptable number? Ideally, you strive for the perfect number 10! Realistically, however, this may look different.

You need to ask yourself, what is the goal, and what is achievable? Moving that number even a little bit can make a massive difference for your client or customer. Think about it: If someone's pain level is off the chart and you can reduce this by even a tiny percentage, I'm confident they would feel this is a huge accomplishment.

Or perhaps you have a client, and the number must arrive full throttle at a perfect 10 for success. Sometimes it boils down to, *how likely is your client or customer willing to follow your suggestions and do what it takes?* Some people refuse to change, even a little bit. Their results will vary significantly from someone willing to take the steps.

I knew someone once who often stated, "I will eat whatever I want and be happy." Several years later, I heard he suffered a heart attack. Who knew?

Side note: We have used a basic 0–10 scale, but some differences exist. For now, a typical 0–10 scale is sufficient. But to give you an example, testing brain numbers can mean very different things, such as depression versus having an overactive brain—a monkey brain some call it.

Earlier, I mentioned an unexpected discovery while helping a client with erectile dysfunction. Using both steps in the testing process, *location* and *magic number*, I found the information necessary to help him. Here is how I did this. I'm a great cook and realized I could easily create a cereal bar with the ingredients on the table. My client loved those bars; he ate them every day, sometimes several bars a day. He was willing to work to make the changes that helped produce the physical result he wanted in his intimate relationship.

I shared these bars with other friends and clients who experienced similar results. Everyone loved them and continued asking for these bars! There were additional benefits, such as weight loss and increased energy. I was so amazed at how well these bars worked that I wrote a book about it. (Please sign up at www.jennellcook.com

for your pre-launch copy; the book includes testimonials and recipe details!)

You have successfully learned how to determine the current magic number for the location of their left kidney. Next, we will tie it together using the last step, moving the needle. We will begin with Step #6. You're doing fantastic!

MOVING THE NEEDLE

We are here, our third step: Moving the Needle. This step determines if we hit our objective and primary goal. How do we measure a favorable or successful outcome for your client or customer? A Simple Health Test using your solution or remedy will indicate how far you can move the needle of our magic number.

As a wellness practitioner or business owner, you offer remedies, products, or solutions to assist your customers or clients in improving their health or solving a problem. Continuing with our example of the left kidney, what would you recommend to this person to move the needle higher from its current magic number of 7?

Here are some product examples of what you might test to help support a kidney weakness or imbalance; you will create your list based on your area of expertise and research.

- Cytozyme KD
- Cranberry juice
- Dandelion root
- Honey calcite

There could be several options; get them all out—whatever they may be for your practice or business. Lay all

the remedies and possible solutions on a table or desk—
herbs, oils, stones, magazine images, supplements, bottles,
or whatever you have.

This time, you will have them hold the item or
product or whatever is in their hand or put it in their
pocket and test them, one at a time. The intention will
be to determine if this solution will work and strengthen
their left kidney.

Here is a recap of where we left off:

1. Are they testable? (Yes.)
2. Get into the 'testing position' with your subject.
3. Point to the location of their left kidney.
4. Make your move over the location of the left
    kidney.

Now we continue to determine how far we can
move the needle.

5. Point to the left kidney location and test by
    pushing down on their extended arm.
6. Is it strong or weak?

You can quickly sort through the remedies to save
time. Eliminate which product, if any, makes the arm
immediately drop or weaken. (Indicating it will not be a
good solution and should be eliminated from the lineup
on the table.) Keep working your way through the items.

Once you have completed testing all possibilities,
you hopefully have one item remaining, possibly even
a few. From here, we discover the best one to move the
needle from its current magic number, 7, to higher. We
have room to improve.

Begin again.

7. This time, have them hold the remaining item(s) that tested strong to discover if it can do the job and increase the current 7. You will be testing these items one at a time.

8. Make your move (wave, brush down, or swipe across the left kidney) and ask out loud (or silently but have your intention clear), "what is the magic number" if you were to use this solution and begin to pulse the left kidney once again.

It will look like this, you are testing, as always, with their arm extended and product in hand (you instruct them to resist). Then push gently for a pulse of one, do it again and pulse twice, pulse for three, and so on until their arm drops. You want to improve their magic number to a 10 or at least move the needle to a higher number than the current 7.

You will have found the best solution or remedy for your client or customer because you have tested the product that can move their needle to its highest magic number. You may have additional instructions or information to improve their kidney to help move the needle further. You have achieved finding the best possible outcome.

A remedy or a solution is viable if it passes each test's acceptable levels. Here are a few suggestions of why a product or solution might not test well. Don't get upset if yours doesn't:

- The product has not been correctly stored.
- The packaging is damaged.
- Manufacturing error.
- Multiple ingredients and one of those is not suitable for this person.

- Expired item.
- It is not suitable for the person currently.
- Manufacturing processes changed from the previous testing
- Ingredients changed.
- Or it isn't good, like the story of my daughter.
- It isn't good 'currently,' and this may change later on as the balance heals.

Here's an example using Andrea's story. She needed a product that took much work to find. We knew it would work well for her based on the previous testing, using only images, as the physical product was unavailable. Eventually, I did find it and shipped it to her. The parcel arrived, and Andrea tested it herself.

She was good at basic testing to determine if something was right for her and tested it out. She found a negative result and called me immediately. Of course, I was very perplexed. I remembered testing the item remotely. I asked her to send a photo of it to me. I agreed; it did not test well. More perplexed, I had her remove the bottle from the box. I had her remove some of the product from the bottle as well. Finally, I determined that the product was good, so it must have been the packaging. She re-tested herself and, this time, got a positive outcome. It does happen and is worth mentioning.

You have completed our three main steps! Celebrate and give yourself three pats on the back! Since you have done so amazingly well with discovering Locations, finding a Magic Number, and how to Move the Needle, let's look at a surprise bonus in the next chapter.

HOW MUCH - HOW OFTEN - HOW LONG

If I were to end our time together here, I would feel good about providing you with a Simple Health Test method to confidently make massive changes for clients, customers, and your business. However, I want to offer more by including additional material taught in my online course.

I discovered some common queries practitioners were asking while researching this book. Need-to-know questions about how many tablets or capsules, for instance, should be recommended. Also, how often should they be taken, and for how long? Excellent questions we can solve right now. How much, how often, and for how long?

We will continue where we left off and begin at step 9. There are three parts to this: how much, how often, and how long. You will test each query separately.

9. Use our continuing example; get your best remedy, whatever you previously tested for the kidney.

10. Have your subject hold the chosen remedy in hand. We will once again make our move (wave, brush down, or swipe across) and ask

with intention, out loud or to yourself, "How many?" and count.

Count as you had previously counted while simultaneously pulsing.

Begin with counting one (push), two (push), three (push), and so on until you reach the desired number. When the arm drops, this will be the 'how many.'

- Let's say their arm dropped on four.
- And that you chose a supplement that we will refer to as ABC.

What does this mean? Your test indicated a need for four capsules per day of ABC supplement to improve the left kidney.

11. Next, you will count and pulse for 'how often' using the same process.

Make your move (wave, brush down, or swipe across) and ask with intention, "How often should ABC product be used?"

Hot Tip: This question is essential; for example, you are testing a tiny animal, and given their size, one tablet per week is more likely. You could crush the tablet using a mortar and pestle to help separate the contents of one tablet over several days or even a week, making it easier to administer only a few grains at a time.

12. Finally, make your move again (wave, brush down, or swipe across) and ask with intention once more to determine how long this product

should be used. You will ask, out loud or to yourself, "for how many days (pulse), weeks (pulse), months (pulse), and even years (pulse)?," if necessary, until the arm drops.

13. In this last step, you will need to make your move one more time and count how many for the second time (meaning the number of days, weeks or months, or even years based on the answer you got in step 12)

14. As always, record your answers for future observation. In this case, the testing outcome based on our example may have looked like this: (as an example)

- ABC product
- Four capsules per day
- For three months

I recommend you add additional details in their notes, such as: this product should be taken between meals on an empty stomach (one hour before meals or two hours after), two capsules taken mid-morning, and two capsules taken mid-afternoon. Many product labels have additional information, like manufacturer suggestions, that you need to consider.

Here is a story about what could go wrong if you don't clarify the information for your client or customer, both verbally and written. (A document we include in our online course.) I recall recommending an essential oil in my early years. Much to my surprise, he neglected to mix the tincture with juice as instructed and used it straight out of the bottle, causing minor throat irritation but nothing serious.

Sometimes, a customer or client cannot swallow products for several reasons, including pets. There are other options we teach.

Wow. You have learned the three main tests and a bonus chapter to clarify how much, how often, and how long. We could end here, but there is one final, significant test I need to share. In the next chapter, I offer an important glimpse into this signature Simple Health Compatibility Test as our grand testing finale!

COMPATIBILITY

Welcome to our Simple Health Compatibility Test, one final technique taught in my online program. I won't get into the entire process, but I will provide a simplified version. You need to be aware of four significant locations that will often come up.

Why do we do this? Because a remedy with a long list of side effects is not the best solution. We know that there are medical emergencies where side effects are inevitable, but this is not what I mean here. You devote so much of your time and energy to your valued clients and customers that you will want to ensure your remedies come with no side effects as much as possible.

I used to hear from my clients and other practitioners about a process of 'getting worse before you get better,' maybe you have to? This idea was never my experience, and I have often wondered if it is because of this compatibility test.

We will now dive into a key part of the process and explore four areas, in no particular order, that you need to check.

These areas are as follows:

- Heart
- Brain
- Stomach
- Cheek

The objective is to determine if what you are testing is compatible (meaning without conflict) with each of the four areas of the body; the order means nothing in this case.

To do this, we will test your item(s) with each of the four areas listed below, one at a time. (Remember to instruct them to resist your push; your intention is essential.)

Side note: I will ask you to hold items near each of the four body parts. Keep the thought in mind 'where and what are you testing,' remember your 'intention.' You don't want your mind wandering about with questions about their gallbladder, your plans later that day, or anything else. Keep your mind and your intentions on task with this vital step.

Stomach

Have your customer or client hold an item to the stomach area, especially if it's a food item. Perform your test to determine if they can easily resist your downward push. You are once again looking for a strong or weak response. The latter suggests an adverse reaction to their stomach if they consume this item, like nausea or cramps.

Heart

Have your customer or client hold an item to the heart area. Perform your test to determine if they can easily resist your downward push. You are once again looking for a strong or weak response. The latter would likely suggest a negative impact on the heart in some way from this item.

Brain

Have your customer or client hold an item to the brain. Perform your test to determine if they can easily resist your downward push. You are once again looking for a strong or weak response. The latter would likely suggest an adverse reaction such as headache or dizziness from this item.

Cheek

Have your customer or client hold an item to either cheek. Perform your test to determine if they can easily resist your downward push. You are once again looking for a strong or weak response. This area of the body often shows up as an allergy or allergic reaction.

Now let's put all four areas together and practice these with a swift and fluid motion; this takes only seconds to complete the testing with each item.

It looks like this:

Hold the item (or image of an item) to the stomach and push. We do this to test this product against the stomach area of the body to determine if there is a reaction, positive or negative. Remember, there is no neutral. Next, hold the item to the heart, the brain (anywhere on the head), and finally, the cheek (either side); each time, push to test.

Hot Tip: Find someone with a peanut allergy and test them using these four areas. Or find someone lactose intolerant and test their stomach with various milk products. The more you experiment, the better you will become and the more confident you will be.

(The full version of a Simple Health Compatibility Test can cover testing of all areas collectively; without needing to test individual locations, saving time and eliminating the possibility of missing crucial areas of the body.)

I share this story demonstrating the power of energy and this testing method. It was beautiful at the waterfront—the perfect location to meet my client and his dogs for a consultation. As a triathlete, he was keen on healthy eating and the many Simple Health Tests for wellness. On this day, we met to test healthy water options for him and his dogs.

We began discussing the harmful effects of cell phones on our energy and ways to combat this. I asked to use my client's cell phone to demonstrate what I meant by electronics interfering with our bodies' energy. Ordinarily, the arm will instantly drop when testing a cell phone at the heart location. However, it didn't work out this way when I demonstrated it. I was utterly baffled.

I had to say or do something, and there were only two choices. I could lie or explain that it wasn't working, and I had no idea why! I was horrified.

I did explain, and much to my surprise, my client gave me the answer. He wore an EMF device that protected the body from electromagnetic frequencies like those from his cell phone. I asked him to remove the protective device, and the demonstration was successful. It wasn't me!

The moral of the story, ensure pockets are emptied and ask questions such as if they are wearing any devices that could interfere with your testing (good or bad); magnetic insoles or jewelry can do the same.

Customers and clients will always appreciate honesty and have never held it against me if I didn't know the answers. It happens. Revisit later, go through the steps again, work together, and you will find the answers you need.

You completed our Simple Health Test advanced skills. A huge congratulations! You've done so well; you should celebrate. I hope to hear about the outstanding results you will create with your clients and customers. Now let's review a few of our key takeaways first.

Top Three Takeaways

1. What location do you think would show up most often?
    Fatigue, hair loss, weight issues, or pain? (Please underline your answer.)

2. Having magic numbers can help you solve more problems.
    True or False? (Please circle your answer.)

3. A product that moves the needle *higher* is not good.
    True or False? (Please circle your answers.)

    Your Final Challenge, If You Agree to Accept It:

    Choose a case study—anyone you want. Your goal is to test them, find any *single* weakness or imbalance, and determine the best possible remedy to move the magic number to a minimum of 50 percent better.
    I accept _____ (Please check here.)

PART 4

Additional Resources

TESTIMONIALS

Thank you for reading this book and for taking the time to learn about my Simple Health Test and the method that saved us. It has forever changed the course of my life. I dedicate everything to the two men who, through their knowledge, made everything possible.

The world needs practitioners like you who want to create transformation and not just help manage symptoms. I know this information can help you accomplish this. Even a tiny takeaway can significantly impact a client or customer.

My mission is to give people the power to be health reliant and less dependent on systems that often fail to meet our needs—information that overwhelms us, savvy marketing, conflicting data, and biased opinions that confuse. This method helps bring clarity in extraordinary ways.

At the back of this book, I have included a few tools to assist you and final thoughts to ponder from my nearly four decades of experience.

Here's a small glimpse into some of the lives I have had the honor and privilege of helping, or teaching, to make transformation possible:

I've known Jennell for more than 20 years. We hit it off right away. I love our engaging conversations, the support we've given each other, and how much we've learned. Digging deep into many topics and researching information is thrilling when we discover new things to help us and others. Along with being a great friend, Jennell has played a significant role in helping me improve my health. She has also helped thousands of others improve their health. Her Simple Health Test method can pinpoint what is happening in your body and provide the correct information to help you heal. She has helped with Lyme disease, anxiety, depression, kidney stones, gallbladder problems, adrenal fatigue, parasites, thyroid problems, hormonal issues, viral and bacterial infections, anemia, digestive issues, allergies, environmental illness, food and chemical sensitivities, and more. With 30+ years in this field and the incredible teachers she learned from, she has vast knowledge and is proficient in using her Simple Health Test method. She's also excellent at teaching this method to others. With all the conversations we've had before writing this book, and because I'm very familiar with her

Simple Health Test method, Jennell asked me to review her book. I am pleased to be here for this part of her fantastic journey. The incredible teachings in this book will allow practitioners and individuals to help pinpoint health issues and get the answers needed for optimal health.

~ B. Backus

"I never had the chance to formally thank you for the help you provided me five-ish years ago. At the time, I was getting vehemently ill with flu-like symptoms twice a year, around late fall, and early spring, for as long as I can remember. I was unaware of any allergies I may have had, but my doctor said numerous times that I didn't have any. I had also developed a gross infection on my lower stomach, which my doctor prescribed a cream for. In addition, I was experiencing severe pain in my feet, and my doctor sent me to a specialist. At my wit's end, after numerous visits to different doctors and a fair amount of money spent on prescriptions and orthotics (no benefits at the time as I worked for myself), I was still experiencing all my ailments. So, I took my brother's advice and contacted you for a consultation. I didn't fully understand what you practiced, but I needed to figure out what else to do. After our consultation… I am happy to report that all my ailments went away within a year. …So, once again, a sincere thank you is long overdue. I still have a medical doctor… I am constantly being referred to other doctors but never to those that do what you do…heal ailments."

~ Sincerely, Mark C

"I have known Jennell Cook for many, many years—about 25 years, since our daughters were in grade school together. She is a very efficient and excellent teacher and healer. She has a way that lets you feel like everything will be okay. When my daughter was eight years old, she experienced severe chest pains. Traditional doctors had run a series of tests on her heart, finding nothing. I was so distraught and didn't know what else to do for my baby girl. One day, while chatting with Jennell, I told her what was happening, and she asked if she could help. I was perplexed. When Jennell explained what she did in her healing practice, I couldn't say 'no,' for it seemed like I was running out of choices for my daughter. Jennell did an analysis and discovered that she had parasites ... suggested a product that would help ... the parasites never returned. This inspired me to take her course... It has changed my life. Jennell can change people's lives for the better. Trust her with your family's needs, and she will bring the gift of wellness into your lives."

~ Lyn H.

"I felt I should write an open letter about my experience with Jennell... I hope this may help those considering this path to good health. I have received treatments and supplements from Jennell for about a year and a half. I have always been an advocate of holistic therapies. The body is amazing in what it can tell you through bioelectrical reflexes of your body. It is merely information about your body that you can use to regain optimal health. I met Jennell at a holistic show and was so impressed. I took many supplements before meeting her but wondered if it was all working. When I found out, she could test my body, and it would tell her what was working or not, I was exhilarated. Now I take what my body says is good for me. Jennell used the information from my body through testing and recommended an eating plan and supplements. Without getting her to check it for me, I will no longer take anything. Now I don't worry if what I take is working or not. I completely trust Jennell, and it has also saved me money because I take what my body needs without guessing. I also like the idea that it can be done through texting. I sometimes send her pictures of products I might want to take, and she tests them for me. I usually get tested every three months or so, and this is because your body changes all the time, and it is a great way to maintain good health and give your body exactly what it needs. It is a non-invasive form of health therapy for the body that works to heal naturally… Addresses the issue! I would very strongly recommend it to others. I would gladly refer my family and friends to Jennell at any time. A great benefit to anyone interested in good health and a better life."

~ Barb G.

"I met with Jennell for testing as an alternative to medication and felt much better with the product she suggested. So glad we met!"

~ Jen - Little Britain, Canada

"Hi, Jennell. Thank you for taking care of my client. She is so happy with the results and is getting healthier. Thanks again; yours in wellness."

~ Monica

"I met Jennell when we were both involved with a nutritional product line in late April 2013. The following year or so, I learned more about what she did... and decided to consult with her after learning of her integrity. In the summer of 2014, I had some issues with my right heel for the past couple of years after I changed my running style from heel striking to forefoot landing. The altered stresses on my foot caused a tendon in my heel to become very painful the next day after a run, to the point I could not put weight on the ball of my foot due to the stress, nor could I step on the heel because that was the location of the injury. Given that the pain was constant no matter what I wore on my feet, but almost unbearable in the mornings, she had me remove my orthotics and start on a product ... Within two weeks, I felt a significant difference. In less than a month, I ran without the pain occurring the next day. ...There have been two incidents where my lungs have been traumatized. Once due to "green" wood chips and another time from horse dander, these events were well over a year apart. In the fall of 2014, I had trouble breathing. Though I couldn't stop coughing, I wasn't coughing anything up. Jennell suggested I use a product for 10 days, and in less than 48 hours, I was gaining relief because I could now cough up what was affecting my lungs. This past February, it was a couple of days before I realized what was happening; again, coughing without discharge, so I called Jennell and told her my story, and again… Less than 48 hours later, I was coughing a discharge and gaining immense relief.

"There have been other incidents as well, but these are by far the most significant due to their immediate impact on my comfort. There are times when Jennell has determined other potential health issues that I could not immediately feel. Still, I trust her and her integrity in her field. I don't question her…and will follow any suggestions regarding health and wellness without question. (Except chocolate.)"

~ Rick C, April 16, 2016

"At one of my sessions with Jennell, she found that I had an issue with my teeth/gums. I had forgotten entirely that I see a periodontist every year. I started taking the product suggested, and there was an improvement at my next appointment. The periodontist takes measurements of your gums. Not only had my measurements remained the same, but some had also improved. My appointment the following year also showed no signs of getting worse. I was thrilled to have that improvement.

"Over the years, Jennell has made many adjustments on me energetically. Sometimes, I feel rough. Suddenly, I'll notice an improvement in how I felt, only to receive a message from Jennell that she had just finished adjusting me. It's quite remarkable. She has adjusted every part of my spine several times. Jennell also taught me a specific move to adjust my SI joint myself. I don't know where I'd be if it weren't for all the help she's provided.

"During another session with Jennell, my acidity reflex was off the charts. She told me what needed to be taken out of my diet and what I needed to add to improve my acidity. I did that and felt better, but acidity flares back up as soon as I go a little off my healthy diet. She also discovered that a large part of my rosacea symptoms was from eating chocolate. I had to give up chocolate; believe me, I didn't want to, but I also liked the rash on my face to disappear. I've had very little chocolate for six weeks, and the rosacea has improved dramatically. Over the holidays, I had a piece of chocolate three days in a row, and my rosacea flared up immediately. Thank you for all you do. I appreciate you."

~ Hugs, Brenda

"I have always had cats in my life. Often bills are costly, and a visit to the vet is traumatic for my kitty. Don't get me wrong; they are often very necessary. Sometimes, however, a Simple Health Test can prove a simple remedy at home. I am sparing my poor kitty and my pocketbook!"

~ Joanne, Canada

"A friend of mine was carrying around a lot of anger and resentment. After seeing Jennell, within five days, he was completely different. I was stunned at how fast it worked. His wife couldn't believe it, and she was so grateful."

~ Brenda

SIMPLE HEALTH TEST STEPS SIMPLIFIED

1. Are you testable?
2. Do you require a stand-in?
3. Are you having trouble? Troubleshoot!
4. Location
5. Magic number(s)
6. Moving the needle
7. The Hows (how many, how often, for how long)
8. Compatibility
9. Record your results!

THE MECHANICS OF TESTING & TERMINOLOGY

Testing Mechanics

1. Have your subject stand in front of you, slightly off to the side.
2. Have your subject extend their left arm parallel to the ground.
3. Place the pad of your left index finger between your subject's eyes (if you are left-handed, switch things around).
4. Place two or three fingers above your subject's left wrist and push down while asking them at the same time, to "resist your downward push."

There will be only one of two outcomes, they <u>can or cannot</u> easily and comfortably resist your push.

5. Use the back of your index finger (turn your finger over) and once again push while asking them to "resist your downward push."

Frequency

While simultaneously counting, a pulse or gentle arm-pump determines an item's frequency or ability to be a good choice.

It would look like this; one (push), two (push), three (push), and so on until the arm drops, indicating the frequency number of the item you tested.

Make Your Move

A wave, brush down or swipe to the side without making contact.

- Over the location
- Over an item

And now, pulse while simultaneously counting.

Pulse

A gentle arm-pumping that looks like this; one (push), two (push), three (push), and so on until the arm drops on a number.

Intention

Intention means you will ask (out loud or to yourself) what you need to know using a Simple Health Test and focus on that, not allowing your mind to wander elsewhere.

FINAL THOUGHTS

Thought #1 ~ When in Doubt, Test it Out

My ex-husband was a shop owner and painter in the automotive industry. He often said, "You can have the best paint job in the world, but if a step is missed in the bodywork or prepping of the vehicle, the best paint job in the world can't cover it up." The steps matter. Follow them. I have had great success using and teaching this method since 1984. Typically this was done live, using hands-on workshops. If you are struggling, and you could be, I invite you to follow me. I have produced video content on my Simple Health Test method. While I have done my best to convey how to use this method with words (and a few illustrations), visual demonstrations can make a big difference. To gain access to this exclusive content, please visit www.jennellcook.com/bonus-video.

Thought #2 ~ Client isn't Ready

Some will be reluctant to follow through and make the changes you suggest. I had a client I deeply cared about; she was an alcoholic and a smoker. For decades we micromanaged her symptoms, never really getting to the source, despite my attempts to have those difficult conversations. I couldn't help her and depleted my energy, continuing to try. Some people are not ready; they have work to do, mentally or emotionally. They identify with and are comfortable with their story. Until they change that, you will have little success. Years later, I took an intensive leadership academy training course and learned some NLP skills (neuro-linguistic programming) that helped serve those customers and clients.

Thought #3 ~ Just Managing

A client came in one day and proclaimed he was a heavy chain smoker, insisting he was not interested in quitting but only in managing the symptoms of his smoking. He was looking for a product to help prolong his life a little longer in a more comfortable way. I struggled with being the practitioner who drew hard lines in the sand about health being a lifestyle. I realized I could help him the way he wanted, but not in the way I wanted. You may have to decide that yourself someday. Where do you draw the line?

Thought #4 ~ My Ah-Ha Moment

I will end by sharing this story that includes a significant ah-ha moment in my profession. My youngest daughter is very strong-willed. We often argue about health and lifestyle. Whenever she had a problem, big or small, I would go into practitioner mode, as if on autopilot, and she would immediately roll her eyes.

She came to me one day regarding an issue slightly more important to her and insisted I "only tell her the parts she needed to know about, that and *nothing* else." At that precise moment, I saw something I had never seen before. Ah-ha!

Thanks to my daughter, I finally understood that some people only want the drive-thru experience and are not interested in the full manual. A future mini-series of books and workshops on niche health topics to better serve you have begun!

Stay tuned.

WORK WITH ME

To my readers:

Many readers request one-on-one services to help them quickly implement my Simple Health Test method into their daily practice or business.

The path to health transformation is knowledge, and I have a deep passion for educating others. Now is the time for us to become innovative with our health. Wherever you currently are and whenever you are ready, there are additional ways we can work together, in person or remotely:

- One-on-one learning
- Group events
- Speaking engagements
- Sign up for the course
- Join our community

Visit www.jennellcook.com today for exciting opportunities available to you!

AUTHOR BIO

Jennell Cook is a Wellness Educator specializing in her Simple Health Test method. A wellness expert for four decades, she co-founded Better Health & Nutrition Centre, a popular health food store and clinic known for its unique testing methods. She is a proud mother and grandmother. When she is not teaching, Jennell can be found gardening or spending time with her animals. She is also the author of Simple Health Recipes (2023) and HeartTalks Volume 1 (2022), a collaborative project. For more information, go to www.jennellcook.com

URGENT PLEA!

Thank You for Reading My Book!
I very much appreciate all of your feedback and
I love hearing what you have to say.

I need your input to make the next version of this
book and my future books better.

Please take two minutes now to
leave a helpful review on
Amazon to let me know what
you thought of the book.

Thanks so much!

Jennell Cook

Printed in Great Britain
by Amazon

30001225R00071